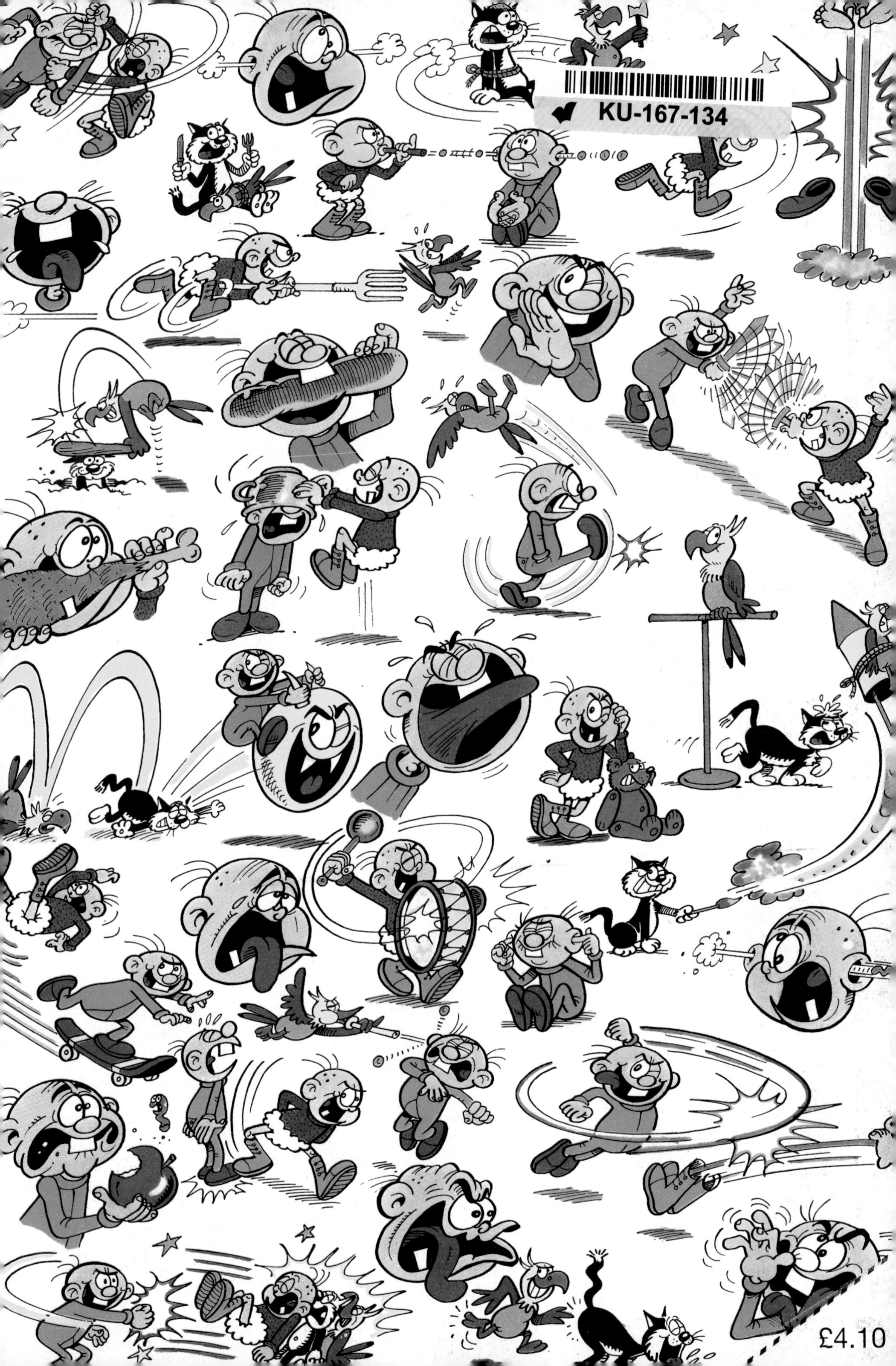

£4.10

The DANDY
CAN'T WAIT TO TAKE A PEEP AT THEM ALL—
KEYHOLE KATE
DESPERATE DAN

Printed and Published in Great Britain
by D. C. THOMSON & CO., LTD., 185 Fleet Street,
London EC4A 2HS.

ISBN 0-85116-531-1

DESPERATE DAN
GRUNT!
HUMPH!
GET THE SHERIFF, THE MARSHAL, THE F.B.I.! DAN'S HOLDING UP THE BANK.
SHAKE!
BANK
RATTLE!
SHAKE!
PESKY PLACE!

IT'S OKAY, MR MAYOR. THAT MEAN BANK MANAGER WON'T LET THE KIDS GET THEIR MONEY . . . SO I'M LENDING A HAND.
HOWL!
ANK
I'M NOT DEALING IN CENTS AND PENNIES. I'M TOO IMPORTANT FOR THAT.
IN THAT CASE I'LL START A BANK FOR THE CACTUSVILLE KIDS.
SOOEEEE!
Dan's a hog calling champ too, you know.
NOW TAKE A MUD BATH IN THIS CLAY, CHUM.
DOLLOP!
OINK?

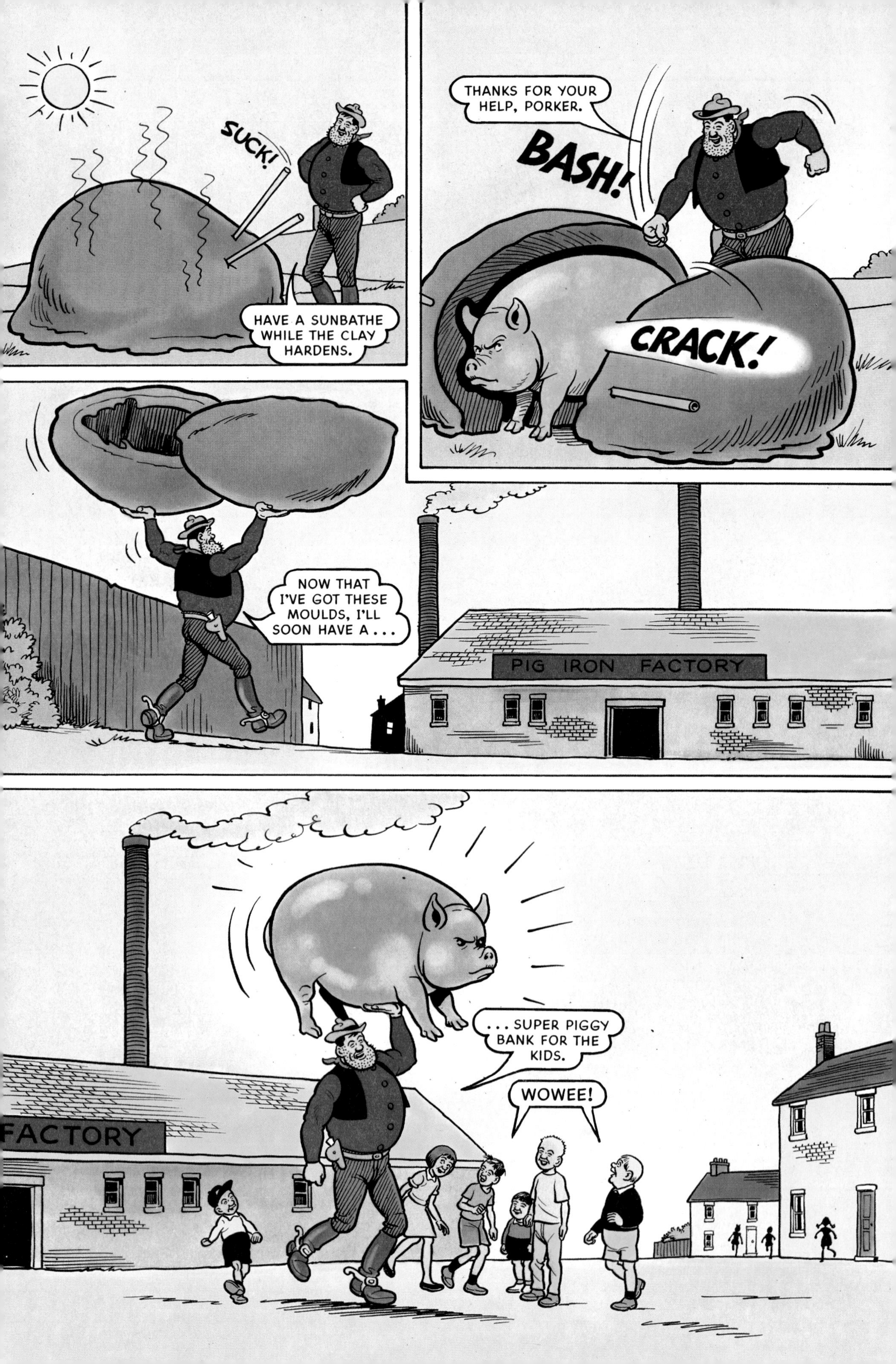
SUCK!
HAVE A SUNBATHE WHILE THE CLAY HARDENS.
THANKS FOR YOUR HELP, PORKER.
BASH!
CRACK!
NOW THAT I'VE GOT THESE MOULDS, I'LL SOON HAVE A . . .
PIG IRON FACTORY
. . . SUPER PIGGY BANK FOR THE KIDS.
WOWEE!
FACTORY

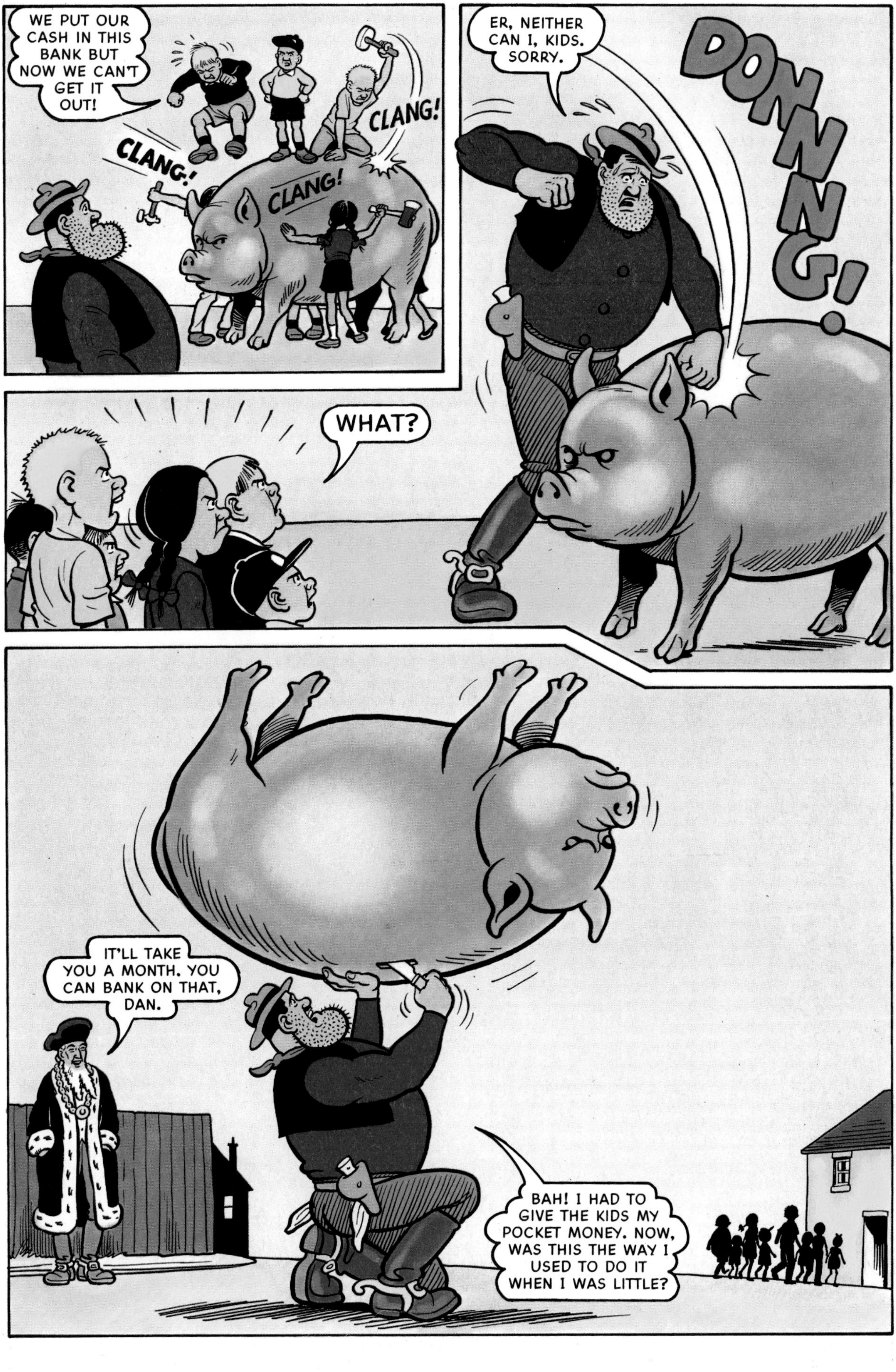
WE PUT OUR CASH IN THIS BANK BUT NOW WE CAN'T GET IT OUT!
CLANG!
CLANG!
CLANG!
ER, NEITHER CAN I, KIDS. SORRY.
DONNNG!
WHAT?
IT'LL TAKE YOU A MONTH. YOU CAN BANK ON THAT, DAN.
BAH! I HAD TO GIVE THE KIDS MY POCKET MONEY. NOW, WAS THIS THE WAY I USED TO DO IT WHEN I WAS LITTLE?

Growing Paynes
LOOK AT MY GREAT NEW TRAINERS, PERCY! BETTER THAN YOUR STUPID-LOOKING THINGS.
WHAT? OH!
WAAGH!
SSH! MUM'LL HEAR YOU.
WHAT'S WRONG, MY LITTLE POPPET?
I WANT TRAINERS LIKE PETER. I'M A BIG BOY NOW — NOT A BABY!
HE'S A PAIN IN THE NECK.

Later —
SHOES
THESE ARE LOVELY, MUM.
OKAY! YOU CAN HAVE THEM.
J2
LOOK! I CAN RUN REALLY FAST NOW.
BE CAREFUL!
TRIP!
YIKES!!

DID MY POOR BABY HURT HIMSELF?
WAAGH! I'M ALL WET.
YOU'LL HAVE TO LEARN TO TIE LACES YOURSELF, PERCY.
YES, MUM, NOW THAT I'M GROWING UP.
So, back home —
PUT ONE END OF THE ROPE UNDER AND THEN . . .
OOH! THIS IS HARD.
SHRIEK! I'M ALL IN KNOTS!
HE'S 'KNOT' VERY BRIGHT, IS HE?
HE'LL SOON LEARN.
I'LL BET YOU FIFTY PENCE YOU CAN'T TIE A PROPER KNOT BEFORE TEA-TIME.
YOU'RE ON, PETER PAYNE!

Percy practises and practises and practises!
WHAT 'KNOTTY' PERSON DID THIS?
LOOK! A 'KNOTTY' CLOTHES LINE.
EEK! MY BEST BRACES!

At last —
STUMP UP! I'VE TIED A KNOT!
WHAT? NO CHANCE!
MUM! PETER WON'T PAY ME! WAAGH!
OOPS! TIME TO MAKE A QUICK EXIT, I THINK.
But —
ER — I TIED YOUR LACES FOR YOU, TOO, PETER. NOW I'LL HAVE MY FIFTY PENCE.
CRUMP!
I BOUGHT LIQUORICE LACES. YUM-YUM!
GRR! I'LL TIE YOU IN KNOTS WHEN I GET THESE UNDONE.

DINAH-MO
WONDER WHERE MO IS?
ZOOM!
PLINK
WOBBLE
ERK! IS THAT SUPPOSED TO BE SOME KIND OF HINT?
WE ONLY USE PLASTIC PLATES WHEN MO'S ABOUT!
HI, MUM!
MP!
DROP!
BOUNCE!
I CAN'T FIND MY SKIMMER AMONGST ALL THESE PLATES!
OOH! MO! TAKE YOUR SKIMMER AND PLAY SOMEWHERE ELSE!
And —
MY FLOWER-BEDS ARE LOOKING LOVELY!

YEERK!
S-L-I-C-E!
OOH! GO AND PLAY SOMEWHERE ELSE, MO!
BAH!
GOT IT! THE PERFECT PLACE FOR MY SKIMMER.
SCHOOL! THE CORRIDORS ARE NICE 'N' LONG!
EEK!
EXPEL HER!
WHIZZ!
ROLL ON RETIREMENT.

Smash Hit
HISTORY
BASH! BLAM! WALLOP!
WHACK!
CLONK!
EVEN IN THE DAYS OF CAVES AND DINOSAURS THERE WAS A SMASHER — I KNOW 'COS I'M HIS DAD!
BLOMP!
THUMP!
SPLASH!
RECIPES
DINOSAUR PIE

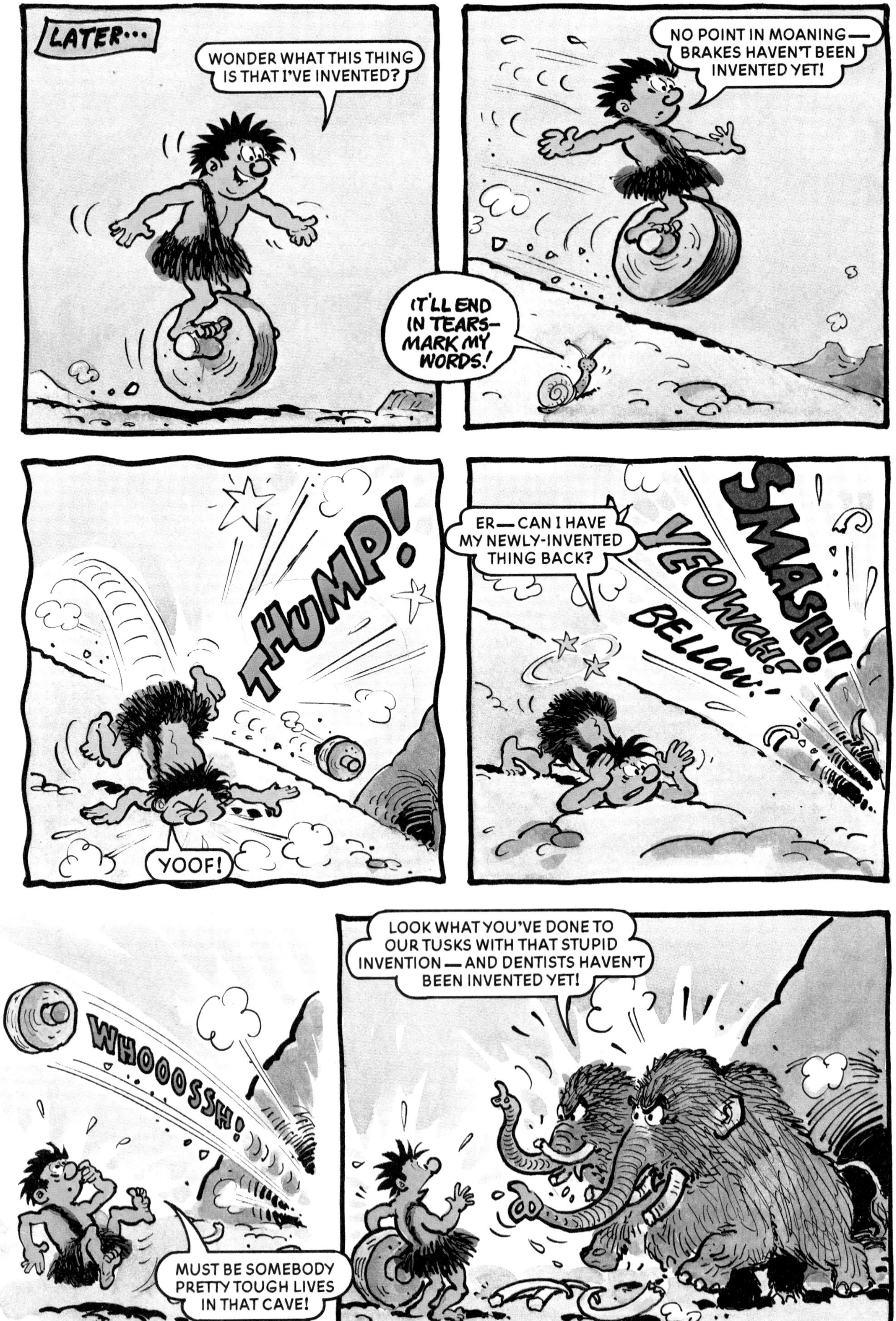
LATER...
WONDER WHAT THIS THING IS THAT I'VE INVENTED?
NO POINT IN MOANING— BRAKES HAVEN'T BEEN INVENTED YET!
IT'LL END IN TEARS-MARK MY WORDS!
THUMP!
YOOF!
ER—CAN I HAVE MY NEWLY-INVENTED THING BACK?
SMASH!
YEOWCH!
BELLOW!
WHOOOOSSH!
MUST BE SOMEBODY PRETTY TOUGH LIVES IN THAT CAVE!
LOOK WHAT YOU'VE DONE TO OUR TUSKS WITH THAT STUPID INVENTION—AND DENTISTS HAVEN'T BEEN INVENTED YET!

TIME TO SCARPER, METHINKS. WONDER WHAT'S OVER THAT HILL?
In a magic flash Smasher was soon to find out!
WHOOOOOOSHH!
AND...!
MMM! WONDER HOW I GOT HERE. STILL, IT'S ONLY A STORY — HOPE THE WRITER KNOWS WHAT HE'S DOING!
VESUVIUS
OH, NO! THAT THING'S GOT A MIND OF ITS OWN. WISH I'D NEVER INVENTED IT!
POMPEII
TWIN-TOWN
BIGGLESWADE
And so the new invention tore through Pompeii—
SMASH!
CRASH!
THWAMP!
SPLOOSH!

...AND TO THINK I TOOK

THE BLAME FOR THAT . . . . !
TOURIST INFORMAT
ER—CAN I HAVE MY THINGUMMYJIG BACK?

Oops! More magic in the air.
WHHOOOOSSHH!
MAKE YOUR HISTORY TEACHER'S DAY—GIVE HIM THE DANDY ANNUAL FOR CHRISTMAS!
WHAT'S THIS—SMASHER THE GREAT?
MMM! I SMELL CAKES BURNING.
KLUNK!
YEOWCH! WHASSAT?
... AND NOW, QUEEN BOADISMASHA?
FORGET ALFRED AND HIS CAKES. LEND ME YOUR WHATCHAMACALLIT — SEEMS ONE OF MINE IS BROKEN.
HM 1
SKRRKKKKCKKK

WE'LL NEVER CATCH HOVISBRED THE RED— HE'S TOO FAST FOR US.
GERONIMO!
HE HASN'T BEEN INVENTED YET, YOUR QUEENSHIP!
SPLUDGE!
HM 1
SMASH!
KERASH!
WHUMPH!
KRACK!
WELL, I DO DECLARE! WE'VE DROPPED IN ON HOVISBRED THE RED! WE'VE GOT HIM ON TOAST NOW!
LATER, IN BOADISMASHA'S CAMP...
WELL DONE, LITTLE MAN— AND THANKS FOR THE USE OF YOUR THINGUMMY. WHEREFORE GOEST THOU NOW?
DON'T ASK ME—ASK THE STORY WRITER!

Oh, oh! Here we go again!
WHOOSH!
AND...
KERACK!
I SAY, WHERE DID YOU COME FROM?
TABLE'S GONE FOR A BURTON, KING ARTHUR. WHAT NOW?
ARISE, SIR SMASHER. YOU'VE JUST GIVEN ME THE IDEA FOR MY FAMOUS ROUND TABLE. WHAT DO YOU CALL THE STONE THING ANYWAY?
DON'T ASK ME, ASK THE STORY WRITER!

Later—
Avalon
TAKE CARE, LITTLE FELLOW.
SCRUMPY MINE
DON'T WORRY. WE'LL BE OKAY, WE'LL TAKE CARE. WE'LL . . . WE'LL, WAIT A MINUTE, THAT'S WHAT I'LL CALL THIS THING A WE'LL!
WHOOOSH!
JUST LIKE KING ARTHUR— CAN'T SPELL FOR TOFFEE! IT'S WHEEL, BOY, NOT WE'LL — NOW BE OFF!
Enter Merlin!
Stand by for more magic!
WHOOOSSH!
NOW, BACK TO THE PRESENT . . .
YOUR SPELLING'S TERRIBLE, SMASHER — CAN'T EVEN SPELL WHEEL!
He's day-dreaming!
AND . . .

GREAT INVENTION, LADDIE, LASTS MUCH LONGER THAN WOOD!
CRACK!
SMASH!
Welcome to HASTINGS
BLOING!
THANKS FOR YOUR HELP, SMASHER. SAVES ME GETTING HIT IN THE EYE WITH AN ARROW!
THANKS, LAD! YOUR INVENTION WORKS A TREAT!
WANTED
R. HOOD & HIS MERRIE MEN
WHUMP!
WANTED
THANKS, SMASHER. DON'T THINK IT WOULD HAVE RUN ON THREE!!
Brian Walker
ENJOY A GIGGLE IN GLORIOUS COMICOLOUR® WITH SMASHER AND ME EVERY WEEK IN "THE DANDY"!
I DON'T CARE WHAT TEACHER SAYS — BET MOST GREAT INVENTORS COULDN'T SPELL!

Ralph the Roman

WHOA! HAVEN'T YOU GOT AN EAR FOR MUSIC?
BOPICUS!
OOH! NOW I'VE GOT CHARIOT-EAR!
THAT'LL TEACH YOU TO LISTEN IN FUTURE.
Inside —
AH, RALPH! YOU'VE COME FOR THE LATEST SONG PERHAPS.
LET ME SING IT FOR YOU.
NO! I NEED TICKETS FOR NERO'S CONCERT.
NO CHANCE! TICKETS ARE AS SCARCE AS HAIR ON A GNAT'S KNEECAP.
AHA! I, SPIVIUS, SPOT A CUSTOMER.
I'LL GIVE YOU THESE TICKETS FOR THE GOLD LAUREL LEAF ON YOUR NOBLE BONCE.
DONE!
WAHOO!
I'LL GET A 'LAUREL' GOLD FOR THIS.

Later—
I'VE GOT PLENTY OF FOOD. A NERO CONCERT WOULDN'T BE THE SAME WITHOUT IT.
And—
I WOULDN'T MISS ONE OF NERO'S CONCERTS FOR ALL THE TEA IN CHINA— AND IT'S NOT EASY TO MISS NERO EITHER.
HE'S THE BIGGEST HIT IN ROME!
I PLAY ON MY LYRE— WITH SOME FIRE!

Cuddles AND Dimples
WE'S FOUND SOME GREAT PICTURES OF US!
PHOTO'S
HEY! THAT ONE'S OF ME'S FIRST TOOF!
YEAH! AND YOUR FIRST BITE TOO!
DAD TOOK THIS ON HIS NEW IDIOT-PROOF CAMERA!
HERE'S OUR FIRST DAY AT PLAY SCHOOL!
PLAY SCHOOL

THIS ONE'S ME TAKIN' ME'S FIRST STEPS.
YEAH, BUT YOU WAS TAKIN' THEM AWAY FROM ME!
AW! HERE'S OUR SECOND!
WE'RE DEAD PHONOGENIC, WE ARE!
HE MEANS PHOTOGENIC!

Suddenly—
FLASH!
ERK! WHASSAT?
SAY 'CHEESE'. YOU'RE MY HEROES!
EEK! HE HAS A CAMERA!
Starstruck fan!
GET LOST! IF YOU WAS SUCH A FAN, YOU'D KNOW WE HATES HAVIN' OUR PICCIES TAKEN.
OOH! ODD BOYS. VERY ODD!

STRANGE HILL SCHOOL
Eddie Potter is an ordinary schoolboy.
In fact he's the only ordinary schoolboy
at an extraordinary school for ghouls.

POTTER, I WANT YOU TO DO ME A FAVOUR.
GULP! ANYTHING YOU SAY, SIR.
THIS IS VICTOR, WHO'S JUST STARTING HERE TODAY. I WANT YOU TO SHOW HIM AROUND AS I CAN TRUST YOU NOT TO EAT HIM.
GREAT! HE'S A NORMAL BOY, JUST LIKE ME!
IT'S A BIT WEIRD HERE, VIC, BUT YOU'LL GET USED TO IT.
THAT'S OKAY. I'M GOING TO MAKE LOTS OF NEW FRIENDS.
VIC, THIS IS MUMMY.
HI, LADS. FANCY A GO?
BLOOD-LIVER-BRAINS-BONES...
DONG!
NO THANKS, I'VE GOT FRIENDS TO MAKE!

AAAGH! WHAT'S THAT?
DON'T WORRY!
IT'S JUST VINCE. HE LIKES A SWOOP EVERY NOW AND THEN.
HI, GUYS. WANT A GAME OF CRICKET? I'VE GOT MY OWN BAT.
NO, TA! I DON'T LIKE CRICKET.
HEY, VIC! WAIT UP!
YEEIKES! THE PLANTS ARE MOVING!
DANGER- MAN-EATER PLANTS

YAAAAH!
IT'S OKAY, VIC! IT'S ONLY WOLF.
HELLO, EDDIE. DO YOU GUYS WANT TO TAKE ME WALKIES?
SORRY, GOT TO RUN. IT'S SCIENCE LESSON NEXT!
STRANGE BOY!
Later —
HEY, EDDIE. I DID IT! I MADE LOTS OF NEW FRIENDS!
BUT HOW? YOU NEVER PLAYED WITH ANYONE.
OH NO!

HMM! I THINK YOUNG VICTOR FRANKENSTEIN WILL FIT IN VERY WELL AT STRANGE HILL!
AW NO! HE'S JUST AS WEIRD AS THE REST OF THEM!
SEE? I MADE THEM ALL MYSELF!
GLUE

NOBODY'S CHILD

WAA . . .
AAA . . .
. . . EEK!
AAIEE . . .
CAREFUL, NEDDY. THESE MARBLES ARE VALUABLE.
YOU CAN KEEP YOUR STUPID WIMPO GAMES.
DANDY
COLA
IT'S BETTER THAN HANGING AROUND ON CORNERS, NEDDY.
KICK THE CAN WAS ANOTHER OF MY FAVOURITES.
GOICK!
I'VE HAD ENOUGH OF YOUR FATHERLY ADVICE.
CAREFUL, NEDDY. I BRUISE EVER SO EASILY.
THERE! YOU CAN HANG AROUND ON A STREET CORNER FOR A WHILE AND GIVE ME PEACE.
WELL, OKAY. BUT JUST THIS ONCE.

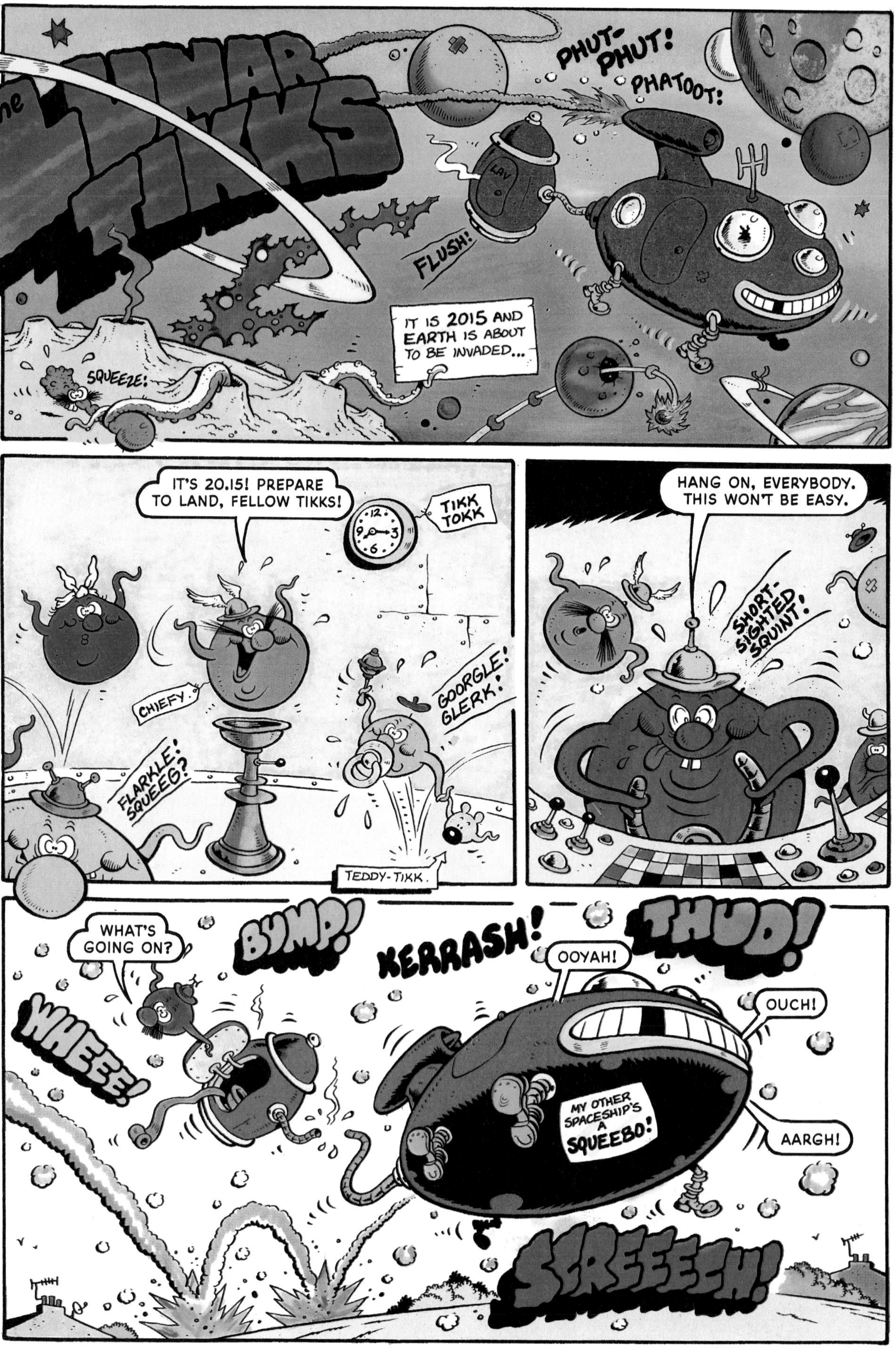
The LUNAR TIKKS
PHUT-PHUT!
PHATOOT!
LAV
FLUSH!
SQUEEZE!
IT IS 2015 AND EARTH IS ABOUT TO BE INVADED...
IT'S 20.15! PREPARE TO LAND, FELLOW TIKKS!
TIKK TOKK
CHIEFY
GOORGLE! GLERK!
FLARKLE! SQUEEG?
TEDDY-TIKK
HANG ON, EVERYBODY. THIS WON'T BE EASY.
SHORT-SIGHTED SQUINT!
WHAT'S GOING ON?
BUMP!
KERRASH!
THUD!
OOYAH!
OUCH!
WHEEE!
MY OTHER SPACESHIP'S A SQUEEBO!
AARGH!
SCREEEEH!

CRUMP!
AH! WE'VE STOPPED!
SKID!
GRR! WHO RUINED MY BULL-DOZING?
SNORE! SNORT! MUTTER!
£3-50 Per lb
PLAYBULL
CUD-FLAVOUR PORRIDGE
BREKKY
FRESHLY SQUEEZED CUD JUICE
RAMBLERS
YOU BLIND BAT! THAT'S THE LAST TIME YOU GET TO DRIVE.
WHOMP!
OOF! HAVE I UPSET YOU?
BLEEGLE!
Then —
AHA! AN EARTH BEING. TAKE ME TO YOUR LEADER.
TICK-STIKK.
WHAP! WHOP!
I'M BEGINNING TO SEE RED.
SMERK
BARP! BELCH!
CHAARGE!
TOSS!
PHWEEEE!
SNORT!
OW! NO NEED TO GET ANNOYED JUST BECAUSE YOU DON'T KNOW THE WAY!
THUNDER OF IRATE HOOVES!
PAINFUL PRANG IN THE PLUMFIPUMP!*
* LUNAR TIKK WORD FOR "BOTTY."

THARRUMPH!
PEEVED PURPLE FURY!
HELP!
CAN I ZAP HIM WITH MY JAMBUTI GUN, CHIEFY? PLEASE, CHIEFY? CAN I?
YES! LET HIM HAVE IT.
SPACE RUSK
MAMA!
BOING: BOING!
POING!
PLUMFIPUMP LOTION
THROBBIN PLUMFIPUMP!
OOPS! MY BARREL'S BENT. I'VE HIT CHIEFY.
SPLAAARPP!
BLEURP!
GLEURB!
Then —
I SMELL JAM!
DRIBBLE!
SCRUMPTIOUS JAMMY WHIFF!
DROOL! SLOOB!
SLURPLE!
LOVELY GRUB.
BUZZZZ!
OUR JAMBUTI GUN IS SUPPOSED TO DRIVE OFF STRANGE CREATURES. IT SEEMS TO BE HAVING THE OPPOSITE EFFECT HERE. OUCH!
ZZZZ!
STING!
PRANG!
JAB!
Back in the Lunar module —
IT WON'T BE EASY TAKING OVER THIS PLANET.
NONSENSE! OUR SUPERIOR INTELLIGENCE WILL SOON OVERCOME THE EARTH PEOPLE.
THROBBIN SNORTLEKONK!*
SNORTLEKONK OINTMENT
THROB!
THROB!
* LUNAR TIKK WORD FOR "HOOTER."
Oh, yeah? Turn to page 113.

SPOTTED DICK
HI, FANS! I'M THE FIRST BRITISH BOY TO GO UP IN THE SHUTTLE!

Blast off —
WHOOSH!
WAHEY! THE G-FORCE HAS KNOCKED SPOTS OFF ME!
HOI! KEEP YOUR SPOTS TO YOURSELF, KID!
OOPS! I FORGOT! THINGS ARE WEIGHTLESS UP HERE — EVEN MY SPOTS!
Close to the moon —
OH, NO! IT'S SPOTTED DICK. KEEP HIM AWAY FROM ME — I'VE ENOUGH CRATERS AND SPOTS AS IT IS!
Later —
WOWEE! I'M GOING FOR A SPACE WALK NOW! AND MY SPOTS HAVE GONE!

HOW ABOUT THIS, TROOPS? BEATS WALKING TO SCHOOL!
Just then —
VELCOME TO SPACE FROM IVAN. I AM ZE FIRST RUSSIAN SCHOOLBOY TO TRAVEL IN SPACE.
HI, IVAN! PLEASED TO MEET YOU!
LET US BE SHAKING ZE HANDS.

YOU'VE GOT SPOTS, IVAN.
DA! ONE OTHER BOY IN THE WORLD HAS SAME TYPE SPOTS — DICK FROM GREAT BRITAIN. DO YOU KNOW HIM?
ER . . . WELL, OH-OH . . . TIME TO GO.
POOR SPOTTY IVAN. I REMEMBER WHEN I WAS LIKE HIM.
Later—
HERE THEY COME.
YIPPEE!
WE HAVE TOUCHDOWN.
I'M BACK, FANS. SMASHING TRIP, BUT LOOK — MY SPOTS ARE BACK.

IMAGINE! IN ALL THAT SPACE AND HI-TEC MACHINERY UP THERE — TRUST ME TO MEET THE ONE GUY WHO COULD GIVE ME BACK MY SPOTS!

SICK JOKES
GOODNESS! YOU SOUND LIKE TOP OF THE POPS, SON.
CRUMBS!
ITCH
CRUNCH
WE HEARD YOU HAD SOMETHING CATCHING.
GET WELL SOON. the GANG
TISSUE
THAT'S IT! BACK TO SCHOOL TOMORROW.
PYONG
VISITING TIME!

BILLY GREEN AND HIS SISTER JEAN
HUH! NO TRISTAN IN THE DANDY. HE WAS MY FAVOURITE.
DANDY
Suddenly—
WHALES SAVE US!
HOI! GIMME THAT BACK, BILLY GREEN.
SORRY, JEAN! I'M COLLECTING PAPER FOR RE-CYCLING.
HAND IT OVER OR IT'S BYE-BYE, BI-PLANE.
OO-ER! YOU WIN.

In the park —
I'VE NEVER DONE THIS BEFORE.
AHEM! YOU'LL SOON PICK IT UP — BUT BE CAREFUL.
Soon after —
AARGH!
WHAT'S THE SILLY FOOL DONE?
CAN'T A GENTLEMAN SLEEP IN PEACE?
I DIDN'T KNOW YOU WERE UNDER THOSE PAPERS. HELP.
GASP! WHEEZE! I'VE MANAGED TO SHAKE HIM OFF. PHEW!
Then —
WOWEE! PAPER!

Much collecting later —
WHERE DID IT ALL COME FROM?
THERE WAS PLENTY KNOCKING ABOUT PEOPLE'S GARDENS.
AHEM! IS THAT SOME MORE KNOCKING?
VERY FUNNY!
KNOCK! KNOCK!
WHAT DO YOU MEAN BY STEALING MY CUSTOMERS' PAPERS? YOU'LL JUST RETURN THEM OR ELSE . . .
WHAT? OO-ER!
AH WELL, BILLY IS RE-CYCLING PAPERS. HO-HO!
BAH! WHAT A LIFE!

DOPEY DINAH
HOW NICE, A LETTER FROM AUNT MARION.
WRITE A LETTER TO YOUR COUSIN MILDRED, DINAH. I'LL SEND IT ALONG WITH THIS LETTER I'M WRITING TO YOUR AUNT.
OKAY, MUM.
WONDER WHAT I'LL WRITE. GRR! THAT REMINDS ME!
SILLY GIRL. YOU HAVEN'T WRITTEN ANYTHING.
MILDRED QUARRELLED WITH ME WHEN SHE WAS HERE LAST, SO I'M NOT SPEAKING TO HER.

CORPORAL CLOTT
This is Corporal Clott, the doziest soldier in the British Army.
Z Z Z
This is the Sergeant-Major, the UNLUCKIEST soldier in the British Army.
WAKEY! WAKEY! RISE AND SHINE!
HUH! WHERE IS THAT IDIOT CLOTT?
ER—I'M UP HERE. YOU MADE ME JUMP SHOUTING LIKE THAT.
Suddenly—
SNAP
OO-ER! THE LIGHT'S GOING DOWN.
See what I meant about being unlucky?
OOPS!
OW!

Soon —
THERE'S A V.I.P. COMING TO INSPECT THE CAMP. GIVE IT A COAT OF PAINT.
YES, SARGE!
IF IT DOESN'T MOVE, PAINT IT. IF IT DOES, SALUTE IT!
LEAVE IT TO ME, SARGE!
MUTTER! GRUMBLE! I ALWAYS GET THE ROTTEN JOBS.
STRIPE ME! I'VE BEEN UNDER-COATED.
Suddenly —
MUST DELIVER THESE STORES TO THE KITCHEN.
THUD
WR34
GENERAL STORES
GENERAL STORES? HE MUST BE THE VISITING V. I. P.
SPLOSH!
WELCOME TO THE CAMP, SIR.
BEANS
HOI!

COVER ME IN PAINT, WOULD YOU? TAKE THAT!
HELP! IT WAS AN ACCIDENT.
I'LL HIDE IN HERE UNTIL HE COOLS DOWN.
AMMO
Soon after—
WHAT A FINE BODY OF MEN. ARE THEY STEADY UNDER FIRE?
AS ROCKS, SIR.
Meanwhile—
THIS SHOULD BE A SAFE SPOT FOR A NAP.
But—
WAGH! A SMELLY SKUNK.
LOOK WHO'S TALKING!
FIRE
DON'T COME NEAR ME. OO-ER!
BOOM!
FIRE
AMMO

OOH! DID I DO THAT?
WHEEE!
BOOM!
BOOM!
MUM!
RUN FOR 'SHELL'-TER.
WE'RE BEING SHELLED.
WAAGH!
HELP!
ER — SORRY, CHAPS. DID I UPSET THE PARADE?
GRR!
GRR!
YOU-YOU . . .
THIS IS ALL YOUR FAULT. HOW ARE WE GOING TO GET DOWN FROM HERE?
I THINK WE'RE GOING TO FIND THAT OUT PRETTY QUICK.

Granny
HMM! I KNOW THE VERY YOUNG GIRL.
SPORT
CLASSIFIED
NICE YOUNG MAN SEEKS YOUNG GORGEOUS GIRL FRIEND! APPLY BOX Nº. 2574
PETS CORNER
ME, OF COURSE. CACKLE!
At the meeting place—
HIYA, HUNKY HIPS. MEET YOUR DREAM GIRL.
HARLEY
TWITCH!
1000
Y'WOT? NIGHTMARE, YOU MEAN.
WAAGH! EVEN MY BIKE DOESN'T FANCY HER.
CAREFUL, DEAR.
VROOOOOO!
Shortly—
YOU CAN TAKE ME FOR A ROMANTIC RUN IN THE COUNTRY.
HARLEY
MUTTER! OKAY. HOLD ONTO YER KNITTING, MISSUS.
ROAR!
HARD ROCK CAFE
OH, GOODY! A QUAINT LITTLE COUNTRY RESTAURANT.
CHORKLE! SOMETHIN' LIKE THAT.
VOOMA-VOOMA!

OUTTA MY WAY. OUR GANG GET SERVED FIRST. TWO CREAM TEAS AND A FAIRY CAKE, PLEASE.
NUDGE!
OOF! WATCH IT, MUSH.
FUME! OAFISH SCRUFFBAG.
MIND IF I CRASH MY HELMET OFF YOUR THICK SKULL?
CLANG!
OO-ER!
DUH!!!
LET'S CELEBRATE WITH A GREASEBALL SPECIAL FOR TWO.
SHE'S FLATTENED PSYCHO CYRIL.
LET'S DUFF HER UP.
AND HER BOYFRIEND.
SLITHER
HOWL!
AAIEE!
SHARE THAT AMONGST YER.
HO-HO! GRANNY'S GREASEBALL SPECIAL'S FLOORED 'EM!
WORRA WOMAN! MY GRANDAD WILL BE DEAD JEALOUS.
GIGGLE! HE MAKES ME FEEL SIXTY-FOUR AGAIN.
VROOM!

BANANAMAN
AAH! THIS IS THE LIFE. SUN, SEA, SAND AND SLURPY DRINKS.
NOW TO BLOW UP MY RUBBER RING.
OUTTA MY WAY, PIPSQUEAK, AND LET A MAN SWAGGER BY.
BLUGH!
HI THERE, CHICK! WHERE'VE YOU BEEN ALL MY HANDSOME LIFE?
HUMPH!
GIRLISH GIGGLE!
HERE, BLOW IN THIS. YOU'VE PLENTY HOT AIR TO SPARE.
GLUMPH!?!

HEE-HEE! THANKS, WINDBAG.
WHEEZE!
HMPH! WHAT A WIMP.
JUST TALK AMONGST YOURSELVES, READERS, WHILE I RELAX BETWEEN PICTURES.
WHASSAT?
PSST!
IT'S YOU — POPPING OFF ON A LONG, UNEXPECTED VOYAGE.
AAIEEE! HIM AGAIN!
Many naughty-cal miles later —
PHEW! IT'S LUCKY I HAVE A BANANA WITH ME.
THERE. IT'LL DO AS AN AIRSTOP.

EEK! ADRIFT IN SHARK-INFESTED WATERS. THINGS CAN'T GET ANY WORSE.
YUM-YUM!
All of a wotsit —
PIECES OF EIGHT! PIECES OF EIGHT!
SCREAM! PIRATES!
AVAST THERE, SEA-LOUSE. AHAR! WHO'S A PRETTY SIGHT THEN?
GULP! IT'S POLLY THE PIRATE AND HIS CREW OF SEADOGS.
WELCOME ABOARD, LAD. WHAT BE YOUR NAME THEN?
ER, LITTLE ERIC, YOUR PIRATESHIP.
OKAY, ERIC THE CABIN BOY! YOU CAN SWAB THE DECKS UNTIL I CAN SEE MY BEAK IN THEM.
SQUAWK! I'M SO WICKED I'M ONLY GOIN' TO FEED YER THIS OVER-RIPE BANANA.
GOILP! OH, GOOD.

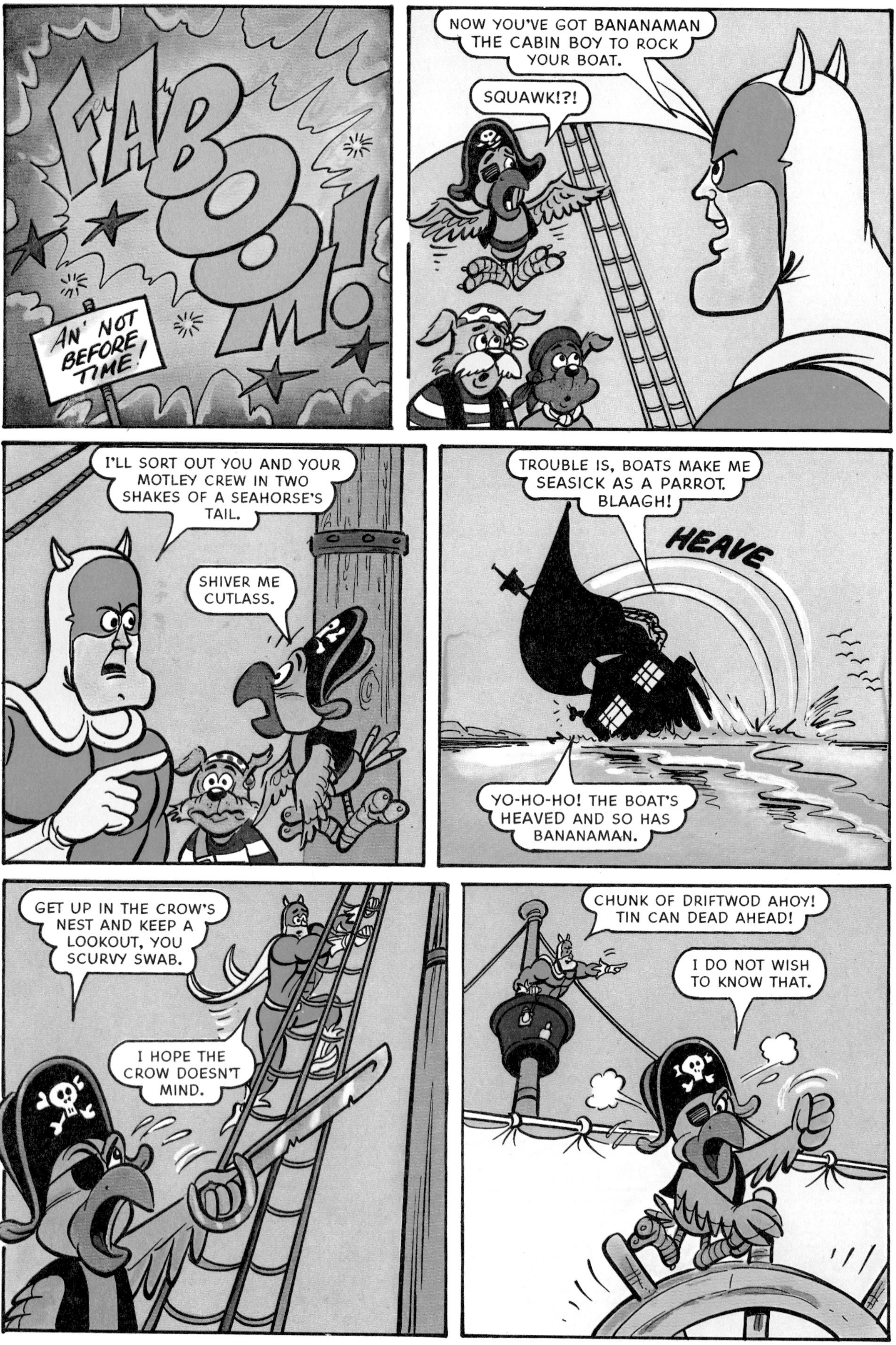
FABOOM!
AN' NOT BEFORE TIME!
NOW YOU'VE GOT BANANAMAN THE CABIN BOY TO ROCK YOUR BOAT.
SQUAWK!?!
I'LL SORT OUT YOU AND YOUR MOTLEY CREW IN TWO SHAKES OF A SEAHORSE'S TAIL.
SHIVER ME CUTLASS.
TROUBLE IS, BOATS MAKE ME SEASICK AS A PARROT. BLAAGH!
HEAVE
YO-HO-HO! THE BOAT'S HEAVED AND SO HAS BANANAMAN.
GET UP IN THE CROW'S NEST AND KEEP A LOOKOUT, YOU SCURVY SWAB.
I HOPE THE CROW DOESN'T MIND.
CHUNK OF DRIFTWOD AHOY! TIN CAN DEAD AHEAD!
I DO NOT WISH TO KNOW THAT.

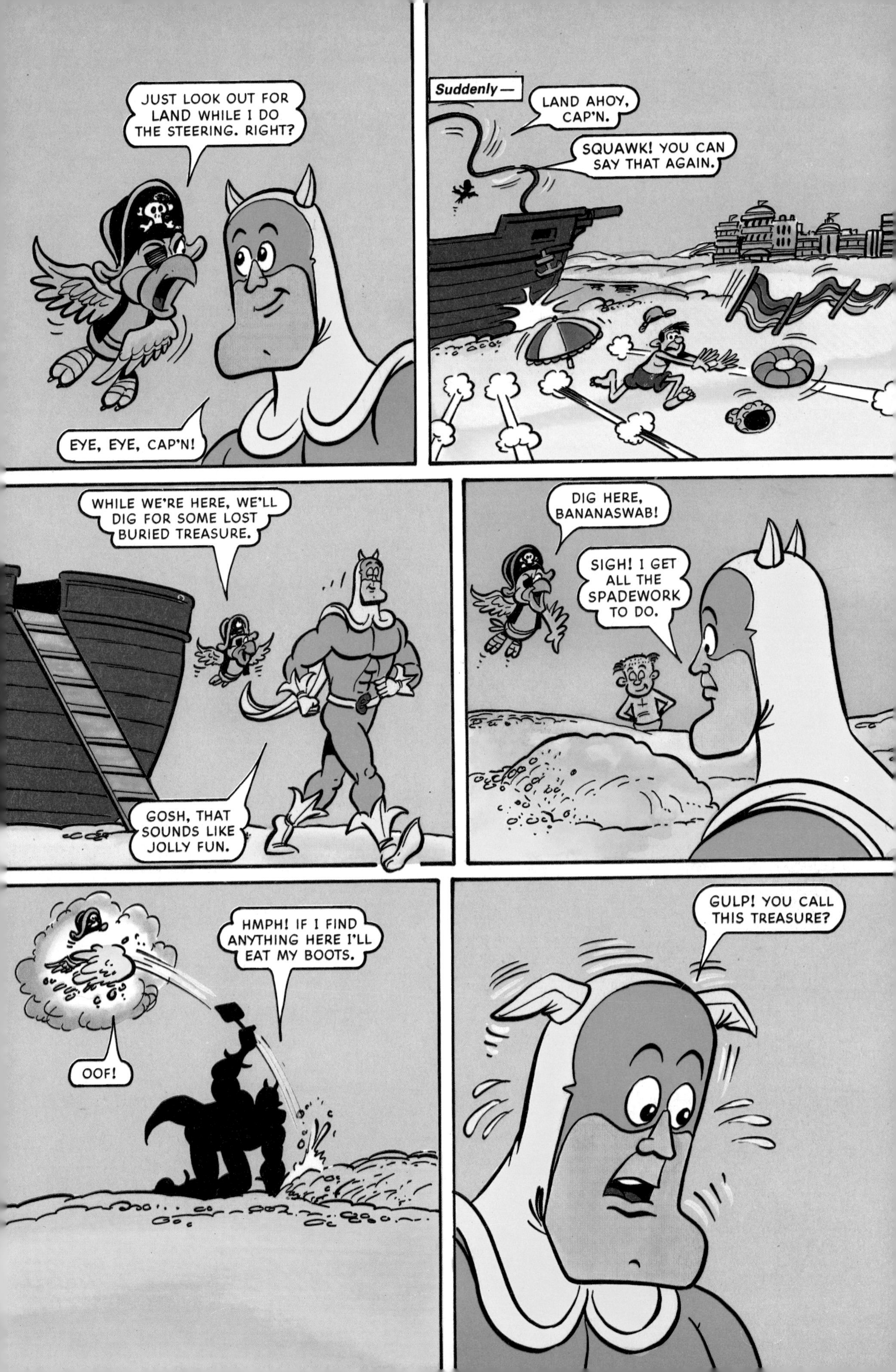
JUST LOOK OUT FOR LAND WHILE I DO THE STEERING. RIGHT?
EYE, EYE, CAP'N!
Suddenly—
LAND AHOY, CAP'N.
SQUAWK! YOU CAN SAY THAT AGAIN.
WHILE WE'RE HERE, WE'LL DIG FOR SOME LOST BURIED TREASURE.
GOSH, THAT SOUNDS LIKE JOLLY FUN.
DIG HERE, BANANASWAB!
SIGH! I GET ALL THE SPADEWORK TO DO.
HMPH! IF I FIND ANYTHING HERE I'LL EAT MY BOOTS.
OOF!
GULP! YOU CALL THIS TREASURE?

IT'S A BURIED STRANDED WHALE!
TEE-HEE! I BURIED HER.
FUME!
PIECES OF FLAB! PIECES OF FLAB!

MM! A HUNKY LITTLE PIRATE. WHAT A TREASURE. MARRY ME!
NO FEAR! I'M HEADING FOR THE SPANISH MAIN.
CHOMP! QUITE TASTY, THESE BOOTS ACTUALLY.

JOE MINCE
SCHOOL REPORT
MATHS - Z MINUS
ENGLISH - PATHETIC
SCIENCE - HASN'T A CLUE
WRITING - TERRIBLE
Headmaster.
I'M STUDYING HARD FOR ME ARITHMETIC EXAM!
BUT THAT'S NATURE STUDY, DIM CHILD. IT HAS NOTHING TO DO WITH ARITHMETIC!
STONE THE CROWS!

EXCUSE MY OLD MAN, NOT VERY BRIGHT, IS HE?
GLURP! HE'S STARTED AGAIN!
IT'S ALL ABOUT ADDERS, THOUGH, ISN'T IT, THICKIE?
ADDERS?! OH, NO! HE ALMOST MADE SENSE THERE. IDIOCY IS CATCHING! SOB!
WHAT DID I TELL YOU, EH? BLINKIN' LOONY, MY DAD, ISN'T HE?
I SOMETIMES WONDER WHERE I GET MY BRAINS FROM!
Next day at school —
ALRIGHT, JOSEPH. YOUR QUESTION NOW!
FIRE AWAY, MAGNUS, YOU'VE STARTED SO I'LL FINISH!

A TAP RUNS AT FOUR LITRES PER MINUTE. HOW LONG TO FILL A TWENTY LITRE BATH?
EXAM.
1 Easy.
2 Peasy.
3 Lemon Squeezy
HARD ONES FIRST, EH?
FOUR HOURS, EIGHTY-FIVE MINUTES AND SEVENTY-THREE SECONDS!
HAR-HAR! WOT A NUTTER!
WELL, I HAD TO TAKE A BUS TO TOWN TO BUY A PLUG FOR THE BATH!
B . . . BUS? T . . . T . . . TOWN? PLUG F . . . FOR THE BATH?!
WHY ME? WHY ME? TAKE THE TABLETS, GOT TO CALM DOWN!
ANOTHER LOONY! I'M SURROUNDED BY NUTCASES!

Once Teacher has calmed down —
I'LL TRY AGAIN. ADD TOGETHER A HALF AND A QUARTER!
OHO! A TRICK QUESTION!
IS THAT HALF AN HOUR OR HALF A SULTANA CAKE?
AH . . . ER . . . UM . . . DITHER!
I'VE ARRANGED A SPECIAL EXAMINATION JUST FOR YOU, JOSEPH!
COR! SMASHING! I'M A SPECIAL CASE, ME!
HEADCASE, MORE LIKE!
I'M HAVING ME HEAD EXAMINED, I AM!
I CAN'T SEE A THING FOR THICK FOG!

KNIGHT LIFE
YOU CAN'T FOOL ME, JESTER. YOU'RE NOT THE BLACK BARON!
GET LOST!
JOUSTING INTERNATIONAL ENGLAND v. SCOTLAND
I PUT ITCHING POWDER INSIDE HIS ARMOUR.
ITCH
ITCH
ITCH
NO CONTEST, SIRE! LORD COWER-DE-CUSTAR HAS DONE A BUNK.

Holiday Haunts!
AH'VE STARTED A TOURIST BUSINESS— BRINGING FOLKS OVER FROM AMERICA TO SEE YOUR BEAUTIFUL BRITISH COUNTRY.
BAH! WE AIN'T SEEN NUTHIN' BUT RAIN.
DAN TOURS
MAP

Then—
THE SUN'S COMIN' OUT. NOW YOU CAN SEE NELSON'S COLUMN.
HUH! MAH CLOTHES POLES BACK IN TEXAS ARE BIGGER.
TAKE US SOME PLACE MORE INTERESTING.
RIGHT, FOLKS! HOLD ON TO YORE BRITCHES! AH'LL TAKE YOU SOME PLACE REALLY EXCITING!
MYSTERY TRIP
LONDON

Soon—
WE'RE IN HAUNTSHIRE! THIS IS THE SPOOKIEST HOUSE IN GHOSTPORT.
HOPE IT'S GOOD — OR YOU'LL BE LOSING ALL US PAYIN' CUSTOMERS.
SCREECH!
Suddenly—
AWOOOO!
WHASSAT? A WEREWOLF?
ER . . . WELL . . .
SCREECH!
AH GUESS YOU COULD BE RIGHT.
IT SOUNDS LIKE SOME POOR SOUL IN TORMENT.

It's Mutt and Moggy!
OOOOOH! HATE YOOOOO!
SCREECH! I'M GONNA MARMALIZE YOU.

Just then—
LOOK! NASTY, LITTLE, GROTTY GREMLINS!

CHEEK! WE'S JUST BEEN PLAYING WIV MUM'S WIGS AND FINGS.
TOURISTS CAN BE VERY CRUEL, CUDDLES!
LET'S TRY ANOTHER ROOM!
MAKE-UP
GLOW BLOB
MAKE UP

HM! AIN'T NUTHIN' HERE BUT BORIN' OLD PICTURES.
LORD McJIM

THERE'S SOMETHIN' FISHY ABOUT THIS UGLY MUG.
LADY McNAB

Suddenly—
ACHOOO!
BLESS YOU!
YIKES!
EEK!
In a passage behind—
THAT WAS A GREAT PEEP-HOLE — BUT IT SURE WAS DUSTY. SNIFF!

Next—
THIS IS THE DINING HALL, FOLKS.
LET'S HAVE SOME GRUB.
WOW! ROAST BEEF OF OLD ENGLAND!

But then—
CREAK!
STOMP!
RATTLE!
CLANK!
OO-ER! GHOSTLY FOOTSTEPS!
AND GHASTLY CHAINS RATTLING.

No, it isn't!
OOH! MY OLD BONES WEREN'T MADE FOR THIS, BRASSNECK.
I LOVE HEAVY METAL. HO-HO!
CREAK!
CLANK!
WOW! THE SILLY FOOL'S LAUGHED HIS HEAD OFF.
HO-OOH!
And—
I'VE GOT NO BODY TO DANCE WITH.
AAIIEE! A GHOSTLESS HEAD!
YIKES!

And next—
DONK!
THERE'S A POLTERGEIST CHUCKING ALL THE DISHES ABOUT!
CRASH!
LET'S GET OUTA HERE!
ZOOM!

I'M NOT A POLTERGEIST. I'M JUST SMASHER. TEE-HEE!

DAN SHOULD BE PLEASED. WE GAVE HIS CUSTOMERS A JOLLY GOOD HAUNTING.
WAAGH!
HELP!
MUVVER!

AH AIN'T PLEASED. THEY ALL RAN OFF WITHOUT PAYIN' ME. GRRRR!
RUN, BRASSNECK — OR HE'LL TURN YOU INTO TINFOIL!
HE'S A BIGGER SMASHER THAN ME.
WE WANTS OUR MUM!
HE'LL BLACKEN MY PEEPERS.
RUN, MUTT! HE'LL HURT YOU MORE THAN I EVER COULD.
FOR ONCE I AGREE WITH YOU, MOGGY.
TERRY BAVE

DOPEY DINAH
HELLO, I WANT TO BE INCLUDED IN THE DANDY BOOK OF RECORDS.
AND WHAT RECORD HAVE YOU BROKEN, DINAH?
I FINISHED A JIGSAW IN 3 MONTHS.
THAT SEEMS RATHER A LONG TIME, DINAH.
WELL, IT SAID 2 — 5 YEARS ON THE BOX.
2 TO 5 YEARS JIGSAW
DOH!

CUDDLES and DIMPLES
WE'S GONNA BE GOOD LIKKLE TOTS TODAY!
IF WE WAS BEING NAUGHTY, WE'D PULL 'AT STRING!
BLUSH!
BUT IT COULD LEAD TO GRANNY'S JUMPER!
SO WE'LL BE GOOD AN' JUST LEAVE IT!
Then —
OOFYAH!
TRIP!

F

OOH! PESTS! WHY DID YOU LEAVE YOUR KITE LYING AROUND?
HUH! MOANING OL' DAD!
WE WAS ONLY NOT BEING NAUGHTY!
YEAH! LET'S NOT BE NAUGHTY FOR MUM!
WHO NEEDS A SILLY OLD WASHING MACHINE?

POOR MUM HASN'T HAD TIME TO DO HER WASHING!
SOAP
WE DO IT FOR HER!
SPLOOSH!
SPLOSH!
Then —
ERK! WHERE'S ALL MY CLEAN IRONING GONE?
OOH! WE WAS ONLY TRYIN' TO HELP!
OOH! YOU SILLY BOYS! DON'T EVER BE SO UN-NAUGHTY AGAIN!
BAH! 'EM ADULTS IS PESTS — THEY'RE NEVER HAPPY!

Winker WATSON
MY ESSAY HAS DISAPPEARED, MR CREEP. I MUST HAVE USED INVISIBLE INK.
NONSENSE! TAKE 500 LINES!
BAH! WOULDN'T IT BE GREAT IF *WE* WERE INVISIBLE? HM?
But they're not! And—
KICKING CANS IS FORBIDDEN. YOU'RE CONFINED TO THE PREP ROOM.
THAT'LL GIVE ME TIME TO THINK OF A WANGLE.
THAT'S TAKEN CARE OF WATSON AND HIS CRONIES.
But soon after—
EEK! THAT LOOKS LIKE WATSON'S UNIFORM. BUT I CAN'T SEE *HIM*. HE'S INVISIBLE.
I MUST BE IMAGINING THINGS.
CREEPY CAN'T SEE THE BLACK THREADS!
Then—
CUT THE THREADS NOW, TROTTY.
OH, NO! HE'S LEFT HIS CLOTHES BEHIND. HE'LL BE COMPLETELY INVISIBLE NOW.

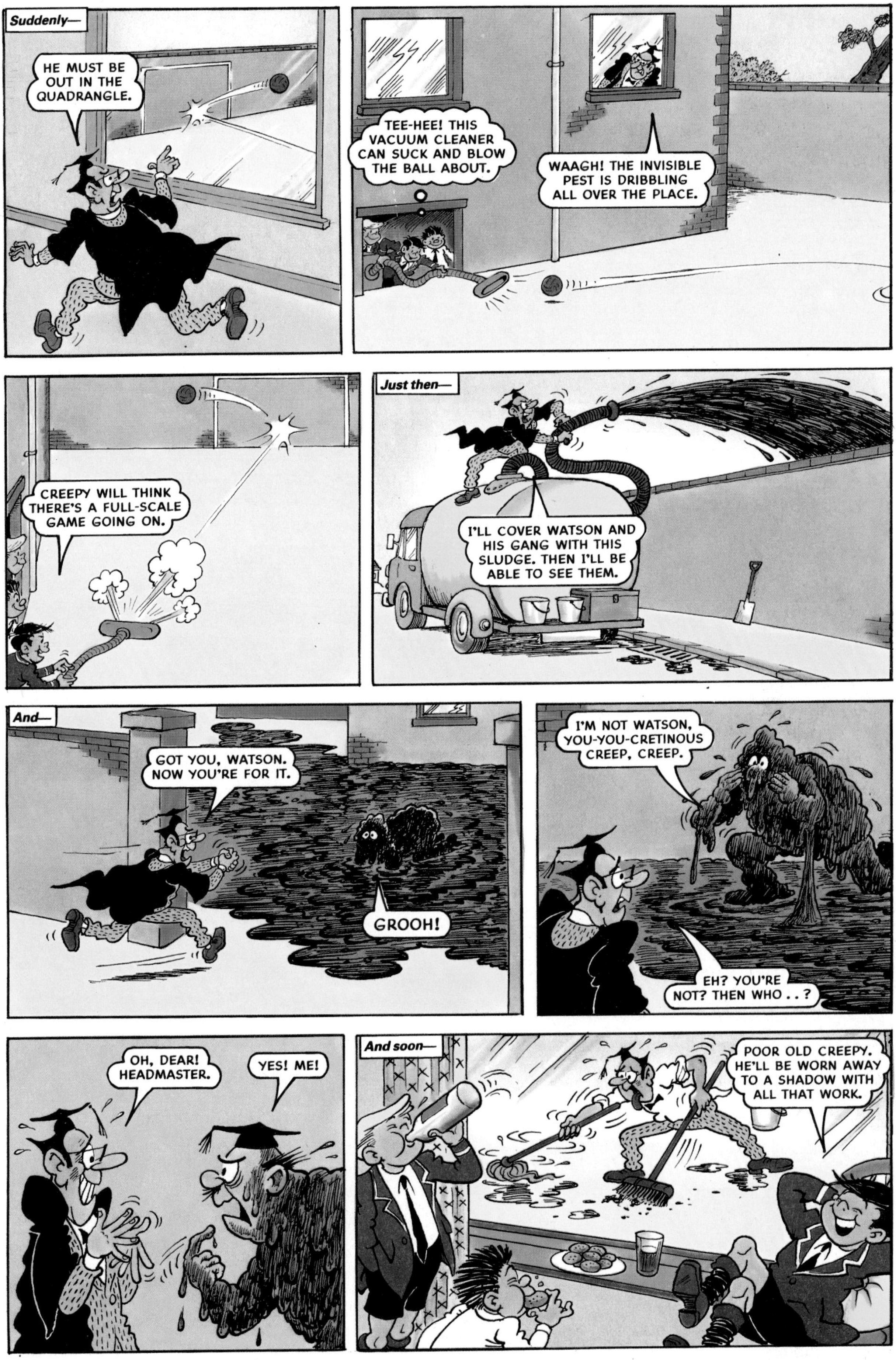
Suddenly—
HE MUST BE OUT IN THE QUADRANGLE.
TEE-HEE! THIS VACUUM CLEANER CAN SUCK AND BLOW THE BALL ABOUT.
WAAGH! THE INVISIBLE PEST IS DRIBBLING ALL OVER THE PLACE.
CREEPY WILL THINK THERE'S A FULL-SCALE GAME GOING ON.
Just then—
I'LL COVER WATSON AND HIS GANG WITH THIS SLUDGE. THEN I'LL BE ABLE TO SEE THEM.
And—
GOT YOU, WATSON. NOW YOU'RE FOR IT.
GROOH!
I'M NOT WATSON, YOU-YOU-CRETINOUS CREEP, CREEP.
EH? YOU'RE NOT? THEN WHO . . ?
OH, DEAR! HEADMASTER.
YES! ME!
And soon—
POOR OLD CREEPY. HE'LL BE WORN AWAY TO A SHADOW WITH ALL THAT WORK.

BROTHER GRIMM
HE'S A SCREAM!
LICKLE JIM
SCREAMIN' 'AIRY 'AB-DABS!
LITTLE JIM'S RATTLE.
SEVERE CASE OF THE WILLIES!
TREMBLE! QUIVER! QUAKE!
GROAN! IT'S GRIM HAVING HIM FOR A LITTLE BROTHER.
DO NOT NIBBLE
GUZZLE!
KRUNCH!
BLERT!
FRIDGE
BE A DEAR AND TAKE YOUR DARLING LITTLE BROTHER, JIMMY, TO THE ZOO.
BUT WHAT IF HE DOESN'T WANT TO GO?
BURSTING WIV MUVYERLY LUV!
SIMPER! TRILL!
SLOOB!
DEEPLY MIFFED!
UTTERLY LIVID!

But no. He's quite keen—
ZOO
GOIN' TO THE ZOO, ZOO, ZOO! HOW ABOUT YOU, YOU, YOU?
GIANT BLUE-TIT-EATING OCTOPUS HOUSE
OINK!
VERY RARE HUNGARIAN HAMMER-HORNED RHINOCEROS.
GALLOP! GALLUMPH!
SIGH!
WOOPSAWOTSIT!?!
ERK!
HURL!
WHELK HOUSE
WILLOUGHBY
HUGE SQUELCHY DOLLOP OF SMELLY GUNGE.
VISITORS MUST NOT FEED THE JUMBOS ~ 'SPECIALLY CURRIED EGGS!
SQUERT! SPLEURGE!
SKID!
?
YODDLEY-DODDLE!
VERY RARE YODELLING WOMBAT HOUSE
SLORKLE! A TASTY YOUNG TITBIT.
WARNING
ATTEMPTING TO BREAK THE "CROCODILE DOWN THE UNDERPANTS" WORLD RECORD IS VERY SILLY INDEED!
GULP!
SNACK!
OH, DEAR! I'M FEELING RATHER DOWN IN THE MOUTH AT THIS MOMENT.

HOP!
NICE CROCKY-WOCKY! SORRY I CAN'T FEED YOU.
KINDLY DO NOT FEED THE DIRTY GREAT CROCS!
PAT! PAT!
MUFFLED SQUAWK!
ZOO-KEEPER FLAVOUR CROC-NOSH
BLURP!
ONE TRIP TO THE REFRESHMENT STALL LATER ...
STUFF! CRAM!
MEGA FIZZY POP
MYEEOWK!
HUGE HAIRY MONKEY HOUSE
BUT YOU'LL HAVE A DRINKY, WON'T YOU?
GLUG! GLUG! GLOOG! GLOOG! GLEEG! GLEEG!
BLOORT! SPLURTER! GLAARGHH!
NIBBLE! SU-UUCK!
BWAARPH!
WAAGH!
GRAB!
HEY! IF IT ISN'T MY BIG BRUVVER!?!
ANYONE CAUGHT FEEDING THE CROCODILES WILL HAVE REVOLTING DOLLOPS OF COLD LUMPY SEMOLINA SQUIRTED DOWN THEIR UNDERPANTS.
MEGA FIZZY POP
SPLAARP!

VOLCANIC FURY!
WH-WHAT IS IT, JIMMY?
BZZZZZ!
MIDGE HOUSE
MEGA FIZZY POP
CROCODILE ENCLOSURE SPONSORED BY THE HIGGINS HANDBAG Co.
BLUEBOTTLE BUTTY.
CLENCH!
DRIP!
HOI! SALESBLOKEY! I WANT A WORD IN YOUR NOSTRIL.
BLAZIN' MAD!
MEGA FIZZY POP
SNACK
WHAT IS IT, YOUNG FELLOW?
TEA
DRAG!
RUB YOUR TUM AN' LICK YOUR LIPS... THEN STUFF YOUR GOB WIV GREASY CHIPS.
OO-ER! JIMMY SEEMS A TRIFLE MIFFED.
EARTH-SHAKING STOMP!
MEGA FIZZY POP
SALAMI
YOU MUST'VE SHOVED MY BROTHER IN THIS BOTTLE AND SOLD HIM TO ME!
WHOP! WHOP! WHOP!
SNACKS
LIMPET HOUSE
HELP! MUVVER! YELP!
HEH! JIMMY CAN BE A RASCAL WHEN HE GETS ANNOYED.

A DESPERATE DITTY

THIS IS A TALE OF YOUR
DESPERATE CHUM.
ONE DAY SO COLD HIS FEET
WENT NUMB.
THE CELLAR WAS EMPTY.
THE FIRE WAS DEAD.
WHY EVEN DAN'S NIGHTCAP
FROZE TO HIS HEAD.
DAN LEFT THE HOUSE. THE
DECISION WAS MADE.
HE ARRIVED AT THE COALMINE
COMPLETE WITH SPADE.
THE MINERS WERE READY
TO GO ON SHIFT,
WHEN UP RUSHED DAN AND
JUMPED IN THEIR LIFT.
BUT HIS WEIGHT WAS TOO GREAT
FOR THE ROPES THAT SUSPEND IT.
THE LIFT HIT THE BOTTOM WITH
A CRASH FIT TO BEND IT.

DAN STOOD AND PONDERED, HIS
MIND FULL OF DOUBT.
HE'D RUINED THE LIFT. HOW
WOULD THEY GET OUT?
HE SAID TO THE MINERS, "WE CAN'T
STAY DOWN HERE.
LET'S ALL GET TO WORK AND DIG
OURSELVES CLEAR."
BUT THE SPADES WERE NO GOOD
IN DAN'S MIGHTY MITTS.
AT THE VERY FIRST STROKE THEY
BROKE INTO BITS.

BUT DAN'S PLENTY TOUGH. HE WOULDN'T GIVE IN.
HE TURNED TO THE MINERS AND SAID WITH A GRIN,
"NOW LISTEN HERE, FELLAS, KEEP CLOSE TO MY FEET.
I'LL BITE A WAY OUT. THIS COAL'S GOOD TO EAT."
DAN CHEWED AND HE CHEWED AND STARTED WITH EASE,
TO GOBBLE THE COAL, LIKE A MOUSE EATS THROUGH CHEESE.
ONLY ONE SNAG. DAN HAD NO WAY OF KNOWING,
THE DIRECTION IN WHICH HIS TUNNEL WAS GOING.
FURTHER AND FURTHER DAN BURROWED AWAY,
AND HE BURST OUT AT LAST IN FULL LIGHT OF DAY.
AS DAN CLAMBERED OUT A VOICE SAID, "HOW DO?"
DAN TURNED AND SPOTTED A GREAT KANGAROO.
YOU SHOULD HAVE SEEN DAN! HE TURNED RED AS A DAHLIA,
FOR HE'D GONE AND BURROWED ALL THE WAY TO AUSTRALIA.
GOBBLE!
BRING ON THE POMS.
NEIGHBOURS

KEYHOLE KATE
BO-RING!
SPLOSH!

WELCOME TO KIDNEY LAND
ENJOY IT, KATE?
NOPE! DEAD ORDINARY!
Two days later—
WELCOME TO DALTON TOWERS
SEE HOW YOU LIKE THIS FUN PARK, KATE!
GHOST TRAIN
HO, HUM! ABOUT AS EXCITING AS WATCHING PAINT DRY!
Later—
WHERE SHALL WE GO NOW? WE'VE DONE ALL THE FUN PARKS.
OH, NO WE HAVEN'T! LEAVE EVERYTHING TO ME!

GOOD! THE ARTIST WHO DRAWS ME IS IN.
99
S. BURGON ARTIST
WHISPER! WHISPER! BIG FAVOUR . . . WHISPER!
99
Later—
COME ON, THERE'S A NEW FUN PARK JUST OPENED.
WE HAVEN'T HEARD.
WELCOME TO KEYHOLE LAND
WAHAY! THANKS, MISTER ARTIST.
HUH! KEYHOLE LAND! MIGHT HAVE GUESSED.
WOWEE! LOOK! A KEYHOLE-SHAPED TUNNEL!
MEGA BORING, ISN'T IT?
I'LL SECOND THAT!
GHOST TRAIN

CHAIRAPLA
HOOPLA
I'M SICK OF KEYHOLES!
. . . AND KEYHOLE-SHAPED CHAIRAPLANES!
DON'T SAY THAT, LASS. THEY'RE MY BREAD AND BUTTER!
ANES
HOOPLA
HOI, MISTER ARTIST. ONE LAST FAVOUR.
So—
THAT'S BETTER! PUT A SMILE ON THEIR FACES . . .
. . . AND NOW!

ZOWEE! HOW DOES THIS KEYHOLE COASTER GRAB YOU?
MEGA BRILL, KATE, MEGA BRILL!
THE BUTLER SAW
UGH THE KEYHOLE)
FORTUNES
HOOPLA
KATE'S
Super Coaster
20p

BRASSNECK
ATHLETIC CLUB
TRIATHLON CHAMPIONSHIPS
BIG PRIZES!
ENTER NOW
WHAT'S A TRIATHLON, CHARLEY?
IT'S TOO TOUGH FOR YOU, BRASSNECK. IT'S SWIMMING, RUNNING, THEN CYCLING.
TRIATHLON, EH? I'LL TRY ANYTHING ONCE.
YOU DON'T EXACTLY SWIM LIKE A FISH, BRASSNECK.
FLAIL!
SPLOSH!
SPLUTTER! YES I DO. I'M FLOUNDER-ING ABOUT. GASP!
RUNNING NEXT. NO BOTHER WITH MY METAL FOOT FLOATS.
FLAP! FLAP!
AND A FURIOUS PEDAL TO THE FINISH. WHERE'S MY WINNER'S TROPHY?
ZOOM!
HEY! THIS IS MY PEDALO, PAL.

ER, THE PROBLEM IS THE COMPETITION'S TOMORROW!
DRAT! I BOLTED TOO SOON.
Next day —
GOOD LUCK, BRASSNECK!
HEH! I DON'T FEEL THE COLD 'COS I'M TOUGH AS STEEL.
VROOOM!
MY PROPELLER FEET MAKE SWIMMING A CINCH.
WOW! WHAT A SPEED!
CREAK! CREAK!
OH, NO! I'M RUSTING UP. I FORGOT THE SEA'S MADE OF WATER.
OIL LOOSEN THE OLD JOINTS FOR MORE SPORTING ACTION. SLICK IDEA, EH?
OIL

MY TELESCOPIC LEGS WILL GET ME INTO MY STRIDE FOR THE SECOND LEG OF THE RACE.
SPLASH!
SPLASH!
GROAN! WE'RE OUT OF OUR DEPTH AGAINST HIM.
HO-HO! WITH MY HYDRAULIC PUMP-ACTION LEGS I'LL GIVE THEM A RUN FOR THEIR . . .
CLANG!
DANGER LOW BRIDGE
. . . WOOFYAH!
WH-WHERE AM I? WH-WHAT AM I DOING HERE?
He's lost his memory.

TRAMPLE!
STAMP!
YEOW! I REMEMBER NOW. THAT'S JOGGED MY MEMORY.
GASP! NOW FOR THE CYCLING EVENT.
FUME! THEY'VE MANGLED MY BIKE. I'VE NO CHANCE NOW.
YOU CAN BORROW MINE, MISTER.
I CAN?!?
TRIATHL
YAAHOO! THANKS TO MY MULTI-PURPOSE LEGS I'VE WON THE TRIATHLON ON A KID'S TRI-CYCLE!
CLICK!
HO-HO! GOOD TRY AT A FINAL WINNING JOKE, BRASSNECK.

BILLY GREEN AND HIS SISTER JEAN
BANG!
THUMP!
THUD!
OOYAH! OUCH!
THAT'S NOT BILLY FIGHTING, IS IT?
NO! I WAS MAKING A CARTIE FOR COLLECTING OLD TINS.
NOW THAT'S A 'CANNY' IDEA.
I BORROWED THE ENGINE OUT OF DAD'S LAWNMOWER.
WAIT! THERE'S SOMETHING WRONG.
IT'S AN ELECTRIC MOWER — AND, ANOTHER THING . . .
AAIIEE!

. . . THE COUNCIL HAVE ALREADY STARTED A CAN COLLECTION SCHEME.
OOF!
CAN COLLECTION
PUT YOUR CANS HERE
Later —
HE'S MAKING A METAL DETECTOR TO FIND BURIED CANS.
And —
TA-DA! WHAT DO YOU THINK? RATHER SMART, EH?
ER — VERY 'ATTRACTIVE'.
I'LL SHOW YOU HOW IT WORKS WITH THE HELP OF A CAN. WATCH.
TINKLE! TINKLE!
SEE? IT WORKS A TREAT!
I'M OFF FOR A TINKLE, TOO.

But then —
DING-A-LING!
OH, NO!
TO THE DUMP, TO THE DUMP, TO THE DUMP, FAT MAN!
WAAAGH!
OH, BROTHER!
OOH! I BET THAT HURT!
OOMPH!
HE WON'T TRY THAT AGAIN. IN FACT, YOU 'CAN' BET ON IT! HO-HO!
Save

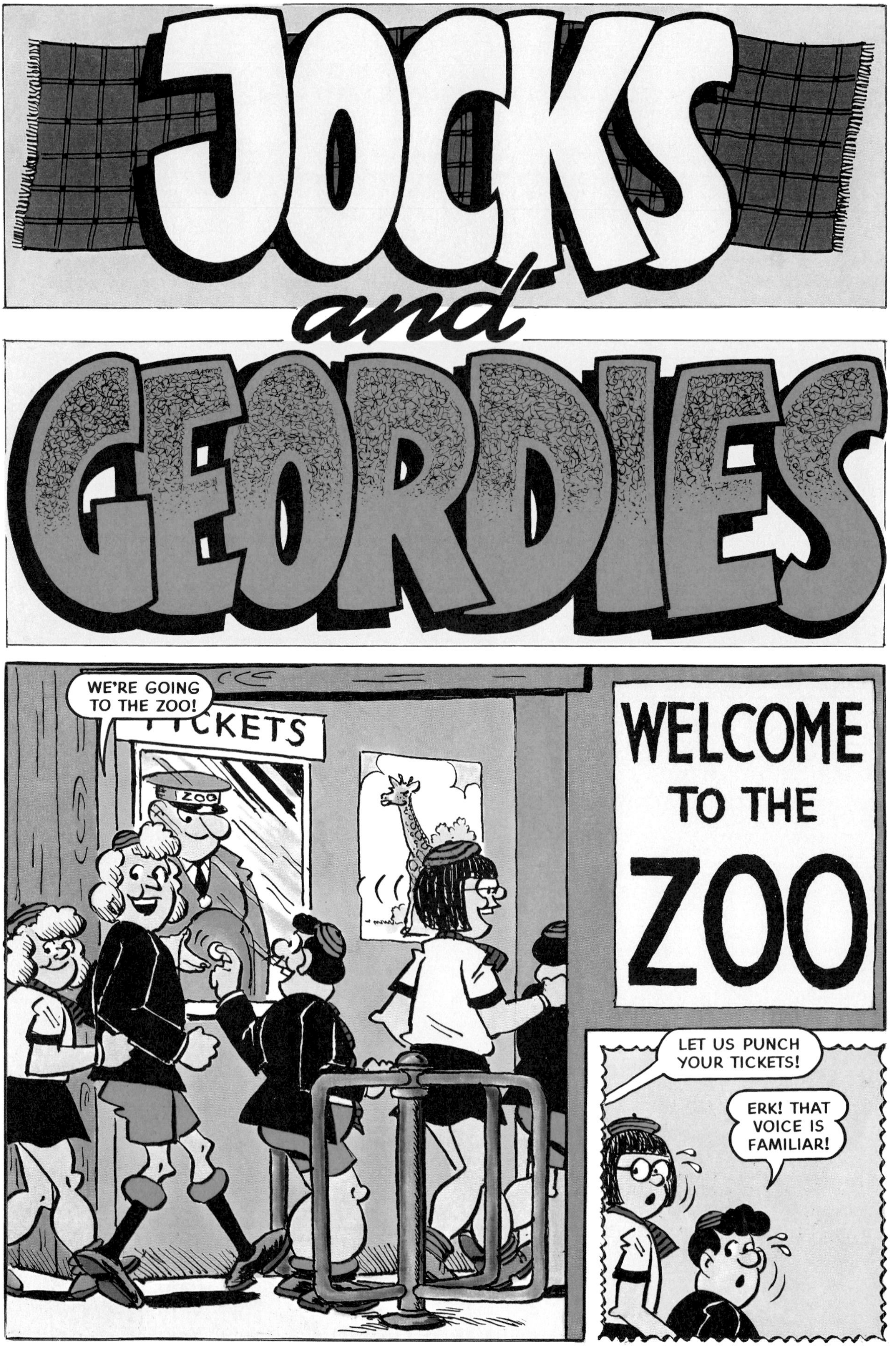
JOCKS
and
GEORDIES
WE'RE GOING TO THE ZOO!
TICKETS
ZOO
WELCOME TO THE ZOO
LET US PUNCH YOUR TICKETS!
ERK! THAT VOICE IS FAMILIAR!

WHUMP!
OOH!
AAH!
HOI! IS THAT MEANT TO BE SOME KIND OF IMPERSONATION OF ME?
BAH!
PANDA
HOO!
And —
BAH! LET'S FEED THE ELEPHANTS!

HERE YOU ARE, EFFYLUMPS!
YEEUCH! THESE ARE BRICK-HARD!
OWW!
OOYAH!
BONK!
AARGH!
HOO! WE FED 'EM ROCK-CAKES!

GROAN! THOSE ROCK CAKES ARE AS HARD AS ROCKS!
HOO! C'MON, LET'S SEE THE PENGUIN PARADE!
HO-HO!
FUNNY, AREN'T THEY?
EASY DOES IT!
PLOP!
HEY!
PLOP!
WHA — ?
PLOP!
ERK!
PLOP!
PLOP!

AARGH!
OOFYAH!

YEEOW!
HELP!
OUCH!

PHEW! WE'VE SHAKEN THEM OFF!
LOOK!
TA!
SWIPE!
ZOO
SQUIRREL FOOD
HOI! WHAT'S THE GAME?
HOO! NUTS TO YOU!
PELT 'EM!
OOYAH!
OWW!
SQUIRREL FOOD
OOH! THIS MEANS WAR!
OOF!
OWW!
ERK! I'M GETTING OUT OF HERE!
ZOO
SQUIRREL FOOD

I'M GONNA HAVE TO DO SOMETHING ABOUT THESE KIDS!
BONK!
I CERTAINLY CAN'T STAY HERE ALL DAY!
HUH?
WHA—?
HOLD ON! HOLD ON! I'VE GOT AN ENCLOSURE YOU'LL BOTH LIKE!
WAVE!
HOO! IN FACT, THIS COULD BE OUR GREATEST ATTRACTION!

GERROUT OF HERE! WE WERE HERE FIRST!
EERK!
RUBBISH! WE WERE!
OOFYAH!
BEWARE. DANGEROUS ANIMALS
ZOO
HOO! THIS LOT COULD KEEP MY ANIMALS ENTERTAINED FOR AGES!

The LUNAR TIKKS
While the Tikks are plotting to take over the planet, Earth, some people are just FLATTENING it!
SLACK ALEC TRYING TO LOSE SOME WEIGHT.
DOCTOR'S ORDERS LOSE WEIGHT OR EXPLODE!
DO NOT STUFF WITH CAKES, BUNS AND GREASY CHIPS
HUGE BLUBBERY BELLY BOUNCING LIKE A GINORMOUS JIGGLY JELLY!
GASP! WHEEZE. I'VE GOT A LOOSE LACE.
AHA! A MEMBER OF THE HUMAN RACE.
WHAT AN UGLY-LOOKING SPECIMEN.
SWEATY PURPLE GASPINGS!
PUFF! I THINK I CAN JUST REACH IT.
NOT A POUND HANGING THE RIGHT WAY.
STRAIN!
Suddenly—
TAKE ME TO YOUR LEADER BEFORE I BLOW YOUR BRAINS OUT!
PROD!
VWOOM!
YIKES! I'VE BEEN OVERDOING IT. I'M SEEING THINGS.
COUGH! SPLUTTER! HOW CAN SUCH A FAT THING MOVE SO FAST?
V18
WORLD LAND SPEED RECORD FOR A PLUMP PERSON.
WE'LL NEVER CONQUER THIS WORLD IF NOBODY STOPS TO LISTEN TO US.
CONTENTED SLOORPLE!
LOOK! OUR PROBLEMS ARE SOLVED.
CUD FLAVOUR INSTANT POT SNACK

RACE MEETING 3 P.M. (BRING LOADS OF DOSH.
THE HUMAN RACE IS HAVING A MEETING HERE. WE'LL LIE IN WAIT FOR THEM.
DIABOLICAL ALIEN PLOTTINGS!
GOOD IDEA, CHIEFY.
FENCE 13
WE CAN HIDE BEHIND THESE HEDGES AND AM-'BUSH' A FEW EARTH BEINGS.
HE'S 'BEING' AWFUL CLEVER!
Later—
THARRUMPH! THARRUMPH! THARRUMPH!
HERE THEY COME. LET'S BLAST THEM WITH OUR STUN GUNS.
LURK!
But—
SNORT!
LEAP!
TOSS!
YIKES! HOOF IT, TIKKS.
HELP! HORRIBLE HAIRIES!
BOING!

Too late—
PADDY O SQUINT ~ THE WORLD'S MOST SHORT-SIGHTED JOCKEY HAS SADDLED UP THE WRONG MOUNT AGAIN.
BOUND!
HURL!
MUVVER!
BUCK!
PRANCE!
LEAP!
JUMP!
SQUIDGE!
PUFF! PECHH! WHEEZE!
RODERICK THE RHINO — IF LOST, KINDLY RETURN TO THE ZOO.
Will
I hereby leave all my pweebs and blitts to posterity
signed FLARDO.
WAFER-THIN INTERGALACTIC BLITHER!
HORRIBLE FEELING OF IMPENDING DOOM!
SQUIMPH!
STAGGER!
REMIND ME TO GIVE CHIEFY A 'TIKKING' OFF.
SQUEEPH! SQUONK!
EXTRA-TERRESTRIAL DENTURES.
SPLURP!
SQUERT!!

THERE'S BEEN A TERRIBLE ACCIDENT. SOME ARE UNRECOGNISABLE AS HUMAN BEINGS.
SNIGGLE!
NEE-NAW! MEE-MAW!
I'VE NEVER SEEN ANYTHING SO TERRIBLE.
BURBLE! SU-UCK!
REMEDY FOR BEING TRAMPLED BY HORSES
BABY COMIC NOT FOR SALE TO ANYONE OVER TWO.
AFTER-COMMOTION LOTION
AMBUL
BLEEBLE! SQUERPH!
HUH! YOU'RE NOT SO BEAUTIFUL YOURSELF.
YOU'LL BE BACK TO NORMAL IN A DAY OR TWO — MAYBE.
ST. MANDY'S HOSPITAL FOR THE HORRIBLY SQUASHED
PATIENTS MUST NOT POUR THEIR EARLY MORNING PORRIDGE DOWN OUR BELOVED MATRON'S BLOOMERS.
GHASTLY GREEN GUNGE
NHS
WE DON'T KNOW WHAT THIS IS BUT IT'S NOT WELL.
Later—
ZOOP!
I MUST CONTACT MY FELLOW TIKKS.
SWITCH ON HOMING BEAMS AND I'LL GET US OUT OF HERE.
MY HOMING DEVICE IS SLIGHTLY BENT. I HOPE IT WORKS.
ME, TOO!
AND ME!
DITTO!
Then—
HOI! IT'S YOUR BRUISES THAT ARE MEANT TO VANISH — NOT YOU!
SCREAMIN' HAIRY HAB-DABS!
SMELLY FEET CURE
GOODBYE, CRUEL WORLD!

Back on board the Lunar craft—
I'LL 'TIKK' THEM OFF AS THEY APPEAR.
CREW LIST
INTER-PLANETARY BEAMER-UPPER
SPACE MOGGY.
Suddenly—
FZZAAAP!
And—
PHAZAAAM!
BAH! WE'RE ALL 'STIKKING' TOGETHER.
SPLOORB! SPLAARRRP! YE-ECHHHH! SQUEEDGE!
OO-ER! IT'LL TAKE AGES TO SORT THIS LOT OUT. I'D BETTER HEAD FOR HOME.
CREW LIST
ZOB
RASSSP! BOO! WHAT A TERRIBLE PLACE!
VAVOOOM!
VWOOM!
VOOM!
And so the Tikks say farewell to the planet, Earth.
YEUCH! WE'RE NEVER GOING THERE AGAIN.
DEAD RIGHT!
THE END

KORKY the CAT
AND THE KITS
QUIETLY DOES IT!
NOW FOR A FEATHERED FEED.
LEAVE THOSE DEFENCELESS SPARROWS ALONE.
AW!
SPOILSPORT!
WE DON'T GIVE UP THAT EASILY.
NO WAY!
TAR
OUR SPARROW DISGUISES WILL FOOL THEM.
TWEET! TWEET!
HOP!
HOP!
HOP!
OO-ER!?!
HO-HO! BIRD-BRAINED TWITS!
YUM-YUM! BIG, PLUMP SPARROWS.
WAAGH! A BIG NASTY SPARROW-HAWK!
WE'RE NOT SPARROWS, HONEST!

NOBODY'S CHILD
Norbert Nobody.
His son, Neddy.
I'M AFRAID I'VE SOME AWFULLY BAD NEWS, NEDDY. IT'S BEEN SNOWING.
ZZZ! Y'WOT?
YABADABADOO!
GNNGH!
Twenty seconds later—
YOU'RE COMIN' SLEDGIN', DAD.
YOU ARE A SILLY BILLY. YOU DON'T EVEN HAVE A SLEDGE.
NO! BUT I HAVE GOT A NICE HELPFUL DAD. WHEEE!
GROOGH! YOU ARE A SCAMPY-WAMPY, NEDDY.
EEKY-POO! I'M HEADING FOR THAT BIG NASTY WALL.
THAT'S A PROBLEM YOU CAN GET YOUR TEETH INTO.

AAIEE!
GNASH!
NOTHIN' FAULTY ABOUT DAD'S BRAKES, OFFICER.
BITING A BOBBY IS A VERY SERIOUS OFFENCE, SIR.
WHIMPER! IT WON'T HAPPEN AGAIN, YOUR POLICEMANSHIP!
THROB!
YAH! BITE HIM AGAIN, DAD.
Back home—
I'M GONNA BUILD A SNOWMAN THAT LOOKS EXACTLY LIKE YOU, DAD.
HOW SWEET OF YOU, YOUNG NEDDY.
NEDDY?!?
SLAM!
BLAARGH!
HYIK-HYIK-HYIK! A DIRECT HIT!
THE GOOD NEWS IS, DAD, THERE WON'T BE A THAW FOR A WEEK.
OH, NO! YOU POOR BOY. YOU WON'T HAVE ME AROUND TO TAKE CARE OF YOU. FORGIVE ME, NEDDY.

DINAH MO
OOH! I'M A FUNKY CROONER, BABY — OOWEEH!

NO! QUIT THAT HORRIBLE DIN!
SPEAK UP, MUM. CAN'T HEAR YOU!
SCREECH!
TWANG!
THAT'S AWFUL, MO. NO MORE GUITAR UNTIL YOU'VE BEEN TO MUSIC LESSONS!
OOYAH! MIND ME PLECTRUM!
And—
SCHOOL OF MUSIC
HALLO, LITTLE MO. YOU MAY PICK ZE INSTRUMENT YOU ARE VANTING TO LEARN!
BET THERE'S NOTHING I LIKE!

But —
HEY! THIS COULD BE GOOD THOUGH!
AH! ZE HORNY FRENCH TUBA THINGY — A WISE CHOICE, MO!
IT NEEDS A FEW EXTRAS THROWN IN, OF COURSE!

And those extras are tennis balls!
PARP!
ERK!

OOFYAH!
OUCH!
AAGH!
EEK!

YOU ARE HAVING TOO MUCH OF ZE PUFF, MO! PICK ANOTHER INSTRUMENT!
THIS'LL DO ME!
BULLSEYE!
ERK!
EEK!

HERE'S MY VERSION OF THE WILLIAM TELL OVERTURE!
STR-E-T-CH!
OOCH!

ZE OVERTURE IS OVER, MO. YOU ARE TOO VIOLINT!
YOU VILL BE HAVING ZE HARP FOR A LESSON!
WHO NEEDS A LESSON?
SILLY GIRL! I DO NOT MEAN ZE MUSIC LESSON.
A ONE-TWO, A ONE-TWO-THREE-FOUR . . .

ZE HARP KEEPS MO CAGED AND TEACHES HER A REAL LESSON, NO?
BAH! CUNNING OLD GOAT!
AGADO— DO-DO!
PARP!
ZZZZ!

DOPEY DINAH
HERE, TRIXIE!
JOHNNY IS WASHING HIS DOG, TRIXIE.
THAT REMINDS ME, I'D BETTER GIVE MY NEW PET A WASH, TOO.
HERE GOES.
SOAP POWDER
NOW DON'T WRIGGLE, GOLDIE, OR DINAH WON'T BE ABLE TO BATH YOU.

Growing Paynes
FLAKES FOR BREAKFAST— AND I'LL MAKE A STEW FOR YOUR LUNCH, PERCY.
CORN FLAKES
WAIL!
CORN FLAKES
WHASSAT?
SNIFF! I WANT TO GO TO SCHOOL DINNERS LIKE PETER.
YOU WOULDN'T LIKE THEM.
OF COURSE HE WOULD.
Soon—
THAT'S TO BUY LUNCH. NOW DON'T EAT ANYTHING NASTY.
I WON'T, MUM.

THE BRAT'S TAKING SCHOOL DINNERS. WE WON'T BE ABLE TO MISBEHAVE OR HE'LL TELL MUM.
LITTLE BROTHERS ARE JUST A PAIN.
At lunchtime—
I GOT LOTS OF GREENS. MUM SAYS THEY'RE GOOD FOR ME.
YEUK! THEY *TURN* FOLK GREEN!
NONSENSE. I'M GOING TO ENJOY THESE SPROUTS.
CAN I SIT HERE, VERA, AWAY FROM THOSE BOYS?
OF COURSE, GERALDINE.
ZIP!
OOPS!
PICK THAT UP.

SOMEONE COULD HAVE SLIPPED ON THIS.
LOOK WHAT YOU'VE DONE.
OOF!
GLOOP!
EEK!
GLUG!
OO-ER! DID I DO THAT?
HO-HO! PERCY GOT ALL THE GROTTY GIRLS IN ONE GO!
Just then—
I HOPE PERCY IS BEING TAKEN CARE OF, HEADMASTER.
NO NEED TO WORRY, MRS PAYNE!
DINING HALL

OH, NO!
TAKE THAT!
ROTTEN FOOD-FROWERS!
WAAGH!
WHAT A GREAT SCRAP PERCY STARTED.
YIPPEE!
OOF!

RALPH the ROMAN
I WONDER WHAT THE SCORES WERE YESTERDAY. HM! LIONS SIXTY, BARBARIANS NIL.
The Roman Standard
Suddenly—
OUCH! A GREEK URN!
WHAT'S A GREEK URN?
TEN DRACHMAS A WEEK.
OH-OH! IT'S SOREBIT, THE GREEK. FETCH MY GLADIATORS.
COME OUT AND FIGHT, YOU SPAGHETTI MUNCHER.
HERE YOU ARE, SIRE.
I SAID 'GLADIATORS' NOT 'GLADIOLAS,' YOU CLOTHED-EARED CRETAN.
SORRY! BUT THE GLADIATORS ARE ALL ON HOLIDAY.
BASHCUS!

GET MY CHARIOT. I'LL GO INTO TOWN FOR HELP!
Soon—
AHA! TRYING TO ESCAPE, EH?
SO-LONG, SOREBIT.
I'LL CATCH YOU IN MY GRECIAN 2000.
NO, YOU WON'T! I'VE GOT A PORTIA.
Meanwhile, at the local stadium—
BAH! THIS IS BORING. I WISH THERE WAS SOMETHING LIVELIER ON.
Then—
BY JOVE! IT'S RALPH.
CROCS AWAY!
EEK! CHARIOT'S ON FIRE.
OO— ER! TIME TO BALE OUT.

WOW! WHAT A SPECTACLE.
LEAP!
OOMPH!
GET OFF MY BACK!
BASH!
THRASH!
TAKE THAT!
OUCH!
OOH!
OW!
Much bashing later—
DOSHIGUS
WELL DONE! WHAT A SNAPPY PERFORMANCE!
BAH! I HATE NERO'S ROTTEN JOKES.

BULLY BEEF and CHIPS

Presently —
I'M SAFE FROM BEEFY'S PAINT-BRUSH HERE!
But —
I WOULDN'T SIT THERE, CHIPS.
OOH! YOU'RE NOT GOING TO PAINT THIS TOO?
NO! THAT'S BEEN DONE ALREADY!
WET PAINT
ERK!
HOO!
LEAP!
And, later —
I WOULDN'T STAND THERE, BEEFY. YOU MIGHT GET PAINTED!
DON'T BE DAFT. WHO'S GONNA PAINT ME?

GRR! IS THAT SUPPOSED TO BE ME?

HOO! THE LOCAL BRANCH OF THE NOT-VERY-FINE ARTS SOCIETY — THAT'S WHO!

pop!